THE LITTLE GOLDEN
FUNNY BOOK

BY
GERTRUDE CRAMPTON
PICTURES BY J. P. MILLER

SIMON AND SCHUSTER · NEW YORK

THE LITTLE GOLDEN BOOKS ARE PREPARED UNDER THE SUPERVISION OF
MARY REED, Ph.D.
FORMERLY OF TEACHERS COLLEGE, COLUMBIA UNIVERSITY

Author and Artist

Gertrude Crampton has written THE GOLDEN CHRISTMAS Book and three popular Little Golden Books, TOOTLE, SCUFFY THE TUGBOAT, and NOISES AND MR. FLIBBERTY-JIB, as well as a shelf of textbooks. Once a teacher, she went on to editing children's books and thence to writing them.

J. P. Miller has designed characters and backgrounds for Disney feature pictures and prepared Navy films during World War II. His first book illustrations were those for Margaret Wise Brown's WONDERFUL STORY BOOK, followed by the Little Golden Books LITTLE PEEWEE and TOMMY'S WONDERFUL RIDES.

The Old Man with a Beard

There was an old man with a beard
Who said, "It is just as I feared!
Two owls and a hen,
Four larks and a wren
Have all built nests in my

Silly Answers to Silly Questions

I fell into a mud puddle," said Jim.
Said Father, "What! With your new pants on?"
Said Jim, "Sure. I didn't have time to take them off."

More Cake

Mother said, "Tommy, what's the matter with your brother?"

Said Tommy, "He's crying because I'm eating my cake and won't give him any."

"Oh," said Mother. "Is his own cake gone?"

"Sure," said Tommy. "And he cried all the time I was eating that, too."

The Amazing Old Man

He seldom or never
    Could see without light,
And yet I've been told he
Could hear in the night.
He has oft been awake
In the daytime, it's said,
And has fallen asleep
As he lay in his bed.

It's reported his tongue
Always moved when he talked,
And he stirred both his arms
And his legs when he walked.
And his walk was so odd
Had you seen him you'd burst,
For one leg or the other
Would always be first.

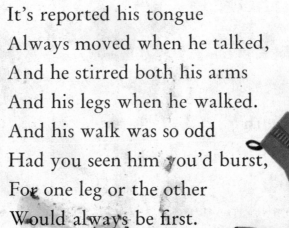

Clowns

Says one clown to another,
  "What's the best way to keep fish from smelling?"
    Says the other clown right back,
"Cut off their noses, of course."

The Owl and the Pussy-Cat

The Owl and the Pussy-Cat went to sea
   In a beautiful pea-green boat;
They took some honey and plenty of money
Wrapped up in a five-pound note.
The Owl looked up to the stars above
And sang to a small guitar,
"Oh, lovely Pussy, Oh Pussy, my love,
What a beautiful Pussy you are,
    You are!
What a beautiful Pussy you are!"

The Owl and the Pussy-Cat

Pussy said to the Owl, "You elegant fowl,
How charmingly sweet you sing!
Oh, let us be married. Too long we have tarried.
But what shall we do for a ring?"

The Owl and the Pussy-Cat

They sailed away for a year and a day,
To the land where the bong-tree grows;
And there in the wood a Piggy-Wig stood,
With a ring at the end of his nose,
    His nose,
With a ring at the end of his nose.

The Owl and the Pussy-Cat

"Dear Pig, are you willing to sell for one shilling
Your ring?" Said the Piggy, "I will."
So they took it away and were married next day
By the Turkey who lives on the hill.
They dined on mince and slices of quince,
Which they ate with a runcible spoon.
And hand in hand, on the edge of the sand,
They danced by the light of the moon,
    The moon,
They danced by the light of the moon.

(EDWARD LEAR)

Smart Aleck

Of course, I don't think it's right to spank a little boy for something he hasn't done! Hurray! I didn't help with the dishes.

Why did you put that mud turtle in your sister's bed? Well, I couldn't find any frogs.

The Nosy Young Lady

There was a young lady of Kent
  Whose nose was most awfully bent.
She followed her nose
One day, I suppose,
And no one knows which way she went!

Poor Hannah!

There was a young lady named Hannah
Who slipped on a peel of banana.
As she lay on her side,
More stars she espied
Than there are in the Star Spangled Banner.

Father William

"Y ou are old, Father William," the young man said,
   "And your teeth are beginning to freeze.
Your favorite daughter has wheels in her head,
And the chickens are eating your knees."

"You are right," said the old man, "I cannot deny
That my troubles are many and great.
But I'll butter my ears on the Fourth of July,
And then I'll be able to skate."

Father William

What is the worst weather for rats and mice?

Weather Man

H ow did you find the weather while you
were away visiting your grandmother?

Oh, I just went outside and there it was.

Questions to Ask at the Beach

Here's another question—What would you do if you were out fishing and the rowboat sank?

Oh, I'd just grab a cake of soap and wash myself ashore.

Here's the question—Suppose you forgot the picnic basket. Why wouldn't you get hungry at the beach?

because you could eat the sand which is there.

hy does a stork stand on one foot?

Because if he lifted the other foot, he'd fall down.

ow can you change a pumpkin into a squash?

Throw it up in the air and it'll come down squash, all right.

Silly Answers to Silly Questions

Why does a hen lay eggs?

If she dropped them, she'd break them.

Why is a cat like the world?

It's fur from one end to the other.

Silly Answers to Silly Questions

When does a dog wear the most clothes?

In the summer, of course. In winter he wears a coat.
But in the summer time he wears a coat and pants.

On which side of a pitcher is the handle?

On the outside, of course.

Look in the Picture

I t goes from town to town, but it never moves.
It runs uphill and downhill, but it is never out
of breath.

What is it?

Why, the road, of course!

Look in the Picture

It has a mouth, but it never speaks.
And it has a bed, but it never sleeps.
What is it?

The river!

W hat is the most wonderful thing to see in the country?

A cowslip under the fence.

What has four legs and flies in the air?

Two robins.

Baggage

What animal took the most luggage into the ark? What animals took the least?

That's easy. The elephant took the most—he took his trunk. The fox and the rooster took the least—only a comb and brush between them.

Animal Questions

What is the difference between a flea and an elephant?

An elephant can have fleas, but a flea can't have elephants.

What would a pig do if he wanted a home?

Tie a knot in his tail and call it a pig's tie.

Counting

What is the difference between a shiny new nickel and an old penny?

Four cents.

Which is bigger — Mr. Bigger or Mr. Bigger's baby?

Mr. Bigger's baby, of course, because he is a little Bigger!

A Smart Solution

Now, then, suppose there are five children in a family, and their mother has only four potatoes. The grocery store is closed because it is supper time. But the mother wants to give each child his fair share of potato. How would she do it?

Mash the potatoes!

The Boat Trip

Across the swiffling waves they went,
　　The gumly bark yoked to and fro;
The jopple crew on pleasure bent,
Galored, "This is a go!"

Beside the poo's'l stood the Gom,
He chirked and murgled in his glee;
While near him, in a grue jipon,
The Bard was quite at sea.

The Boat Trip

"Gallop! Golloy! Thou scrumjous Bard!
Take pen or pencil and endite
A pome. My brain needs kurgling hard,
And I will feast tonight."

That wansome Bard he took his pen,
A flirgly look around he guv;
He squoffled once, he squirled, and then
He wrote what's writ above.

You Tell 'Em

You tell 'em, Bean.
He's been stringing you.

You tell 'em, Cat.
That's what you're fur.

You tell 'em Custard Pie.
You've got a crust.

You tell 'em, June,
And don't July.

You Tell 'Em Again!

You tell 'em, Hard-boiled Egg.
You can't be beat.

You tell 'em, Horse.
You carry a tail.

You tell 'em, Tree.
You've got the bark.

You tell 'em, Submarine.
I can't seaplane.

Mother said, "Mary Lou, what do you want to take your cod liver oil with?"

"With a fork."

Doctor, what is the difference between a bottle of your medicine and a naughty boy?

"One is well shaken before taken. The other is taken and well shaken!"

W hat did the old woman say when she looked into the empty barrel?

OICURMT

W hat never asks a question but always has to be answered?

The telephone.

The Animal Fair

I went to the Animal Fair.
The birds and the beasts were there.
The big baboon, by the light of the moon,
Was combing his auburn hair.

The Animal Fair

The monkey, he got drunk
And sat on the elephant's trunk.
The elephant sneezed and fell on his knees
And what became of the monk, the monk. the monk . . .

Table Manners

Johnny, I wish you'd stop reaching for things.
   Haven't you got a tongue?"
"Yes, Mother. But my arm is longer."

I eat my peas with honey;
   I've done it all my life.
They do taste kind of funny,
   But it keeps them on my knife.

Flea, Fly, Flew, Flue!

A flea and a fly in a flue
    Were imprisoned;
So what could they do?
Said the fly, "Let us flee!"
"Let us fly!" said the flea.
And they flew through a flaw in the flue!